FuN aNd GaMes

Shake rattle roll!

Text and illustrations
by Hilda Offen

© This edition
Baby's First Book Club
Bristol, PA 19907-9541

Text and illustrations:
Copyright © Hilda Offen 1992, 1993 and 1994.
First Published by Random House U.K. 1997.
Original title: "Fun and Games".

ISBN 1-881445-94-1
Printed in Italy

A Fox
Got My Socks

On a sunny washing day,

Pretend to wash clothes.

my clothes flip-flapped
and blew away.

Flap arms.

A cat got my hat.

Touch head with both hands.

A fox got my socks.

Touch feet.

A goat got my coat.

Pretend to fasten buttons.

An owl got my towel.

Pretend to flap towel.

"Oh no!" said the pig.
"These pants are too big!"

Pretend to hold up pants.

And the bear gave a snort:
"This sweater's too short!"

Pull up sweater.

Two baby llamas
were in my pajamas.

Pretend to touch pajama top and bottom.

My scarf made me laugh,
wrapped around a giraffe.

Pretend to wrap scarf around your neck.

But the sun was so hot,

Fan face.

I said, "Keep what you've got."   *Hold out arms.*

"Because...

…I'm happy enough
without all that stuff!"

Dance around.

The Sheep
Made a Leap

Ladies and gentlemen—
the show's starting now!

Spread arms.

The audience clapped,

Grown-ups clap.

and my friends took a bow.

Bow.

First two little crows
pointed their toes.

Point toes.

Then two baby seals
rolled head over heels.

Do a somersault.

The sheep made a leap.

Jump in the air.

And the pig twirled around.

Twirl around.

The bear made us laugh

Everyone laugh.

when he fell to the ground.   *Fall down.*

The monkey stretched his arms out wide.

Stretch out arms.

The hippo swayed from side to side.

Sway from side to side.

When everyone stamped
and yelled for more,

Roll around.

the big gray elephant
rolled on the floor.

Grown-ups stamp and yell.

We all danced around
and kicked our legs high.

Dance around and kick legs.

Then the curtain came down,
and we all waved good-bye!

Wave.

As Quiet
as a Mouse

I was as quiet as a mouse,
I tiptoed all around.

Put finger to lips.
Walk on tiptoe.

I listened and listened,
but there wasn't a sound.

Put hand to ear.

Sigh.

Then…a gold butterfly
breathed a long sigh.

A worm gave a wiggle
and started to giggle.

Giggle.

"A-choo!" sneezed the hen.
Then she did it again.

Pretend to sneeze twice.

The pig was so bored
that she lay down and snored.

Snore.

"Clap your hands, girls and boys!"
said the seal. "Make a noise."

Clap your hands.

The chimp said, "I'm champ,"
and started to stamp.

Stamp your feet.

"You?" said the giraffe.
"Oh, don't make me laugh!"

Laugh.

The bear gave a shout,
"The wolf's here, look out!"

Shout "Look out!"

The wolf said, "I'm tough.
I'll huff and I'll puff!"

Huff and puff.

Then the dinosaur roared,
and he roared and he ROARED!

Roar.

What a terrible din!
What a noise! What a sound!

Sigh, giggle, sneeze, snore, clap, stamp, laugh, shout, huff and puff, and roar.

I told them to stop!
And they all turned around.

Shout "Stop!"

I made them be quiet.
It didn't take long.

Whisper "Shhh!"

Then they danced in a circle
while I sang them a song.

Sing your favorite song.